The Picture Book of
SALT

ANITA BROOKS

80022

The John Day Company   New York

By Anita Brooks

THE PICTURE BOOK OF FISHERIES
THE PICTURE BOOK OF TEA AND COFFEE
THE PICTURE BOOK OF GRAINS
THE PICTURE BOOK OF SALT

© 1964 by Anita Brooks

Library of Congress Catalogue Card Number: 64-10451

MANUFACTURED IN THE UNITED STATES OF AMERICA

CONTENTS

ACKNOWLEDGMENTS

I owe a large debt of gratitude to Claire Hurwitt whose imaginative, thoughtful and unflagging research provided me with much of the material for this book; to The Salt Institute for facts about salt production, uses, and historical background; to the many information bureaus of national consulates for their generosity and patience in providing me with photographs; to Pauline Thurman, photograph librarian of the Pan American Union in Washington, D.C., for her very kind attention in connection with this and other books in the series; and to all those in the salt industry whose names appear in credit lines throughout the book. My thanks and appreciation go also to Joy Dryfoos, of Research, Writing, Editing Associates, for help in getting me off to a good start.

Since salt has always been a symbol for wit, wisdom, and enduring friendship, I can, with equanimity and pleasure, dedicate this book to my son, Henry Stanford Brooks, who has already shown himself to have these qualities in good measure.

Anita Brooks

New York City, 1963

PREFACE

Salt has been called the oldest article of commerce. Its history is woven into the fabric of man's own existence since the beginning of time, for without salt in some form, neither man nor his animals could go on living much longer than a month.

Today, most of the world takes salt for granted. We forget that in the past men fought and died to possess some of the precious white crystals. We forget that many of the world's roadways and highways are built along the old salt caravan routes in Europe and Asia; and, in America, over the old salt trails. We remember hearing of fabulous Timbuktu, but we forget that this once rich and exotic African city was the center of the salt trade. We forget that salt has been used as money in almost every country, that it was and still is part of many customs and religious rites. The Old Testament reminds us that of all sacred agreements the "Covenant of Salt" was considered the most binding, for salt represents purity and steadfastness. And the expression "salt of the earth" reminds us that salt has always been a symbol for quality and enduring friendship.

In this book we learn salt's chemical name and see where it is found and how it is manufactured. We see it in some of its most spectacular natural forms, and learn how people all over the world "harvest" it from the sea, or mine it from deep in the earth. We see the rock salt mines — great underground caverns that begin to look like cathedrals and, sometimes, do become places of worship.

Above all, we learn that not only is salt found in the sea and the earth but in all men. It is part of their blood, sweat, and tears.

THREE WAYS WE OBTAIN SALT

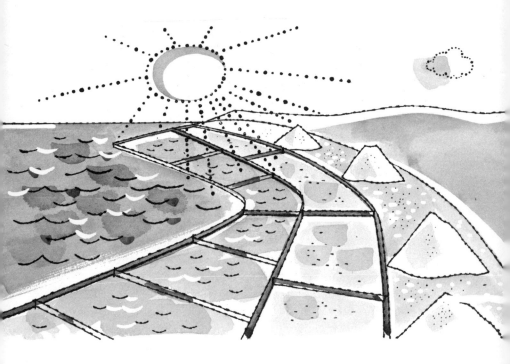

From the Waters of the Earth (Evaporation or Solar Method)

From Inside the Earth (Salt Mines)

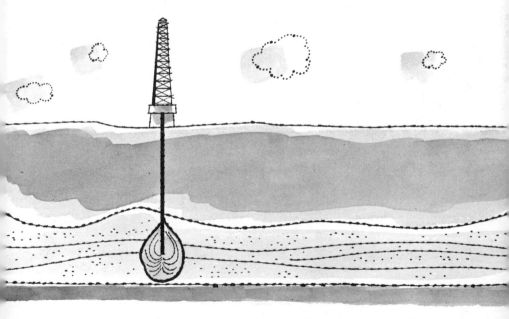

Wells to Salt Layers in the Earth (Hydraulic Mining)

**SALT
FROM THE SEA**

Eastfoto

There is salt in the sea, the earth, and even in man himself. It is found in his blood, sweat, and tears, and we know now that all animal life must have some form of salt to go on living. For this reason, the history of salt has been part of man's own history since the beginning of time. There is no written record of when or how its discovery first took place, but we find it mentioned many times in the Bible. In Biblical days, salt was harvested from the sea. These tiny windmills are on a salt farm in a small village in Lebanon where the people make salt just as it was made over a thousand years ago.

United Press International

Man began very early to invent ways to take salt out of sea-water. He discovered that if he blocked off the seawater in small ponds, or drew it up from natural wells and set it out in some kind of container, the sun would dry up (evaporate) the water. There, on the bottom, would be left a layer of the white crystals so important to him. This method of making salt is called the *solar* process. In ancient days it was hard, hot work. Everything had to be done by hand, as you can see here. The sea in the distance is the Arabian Sea.

Inland, man got his salt from natural salt springs, or by haul-
ing up salty water, called *brine*, from wells. To get the salt
from the water, he cooked the brine over fires. This man is
using the old method today in a Laotian village near Vien-
tiane.

This is a slab of salt taken from the sea on the coast of Venezuela, S. A. Here, ocean water is drained into low flats where the salt forms in layers two to three inches thick. Workmen break up the layers with their feet and float them ashore in barges to dry in the sun. The salt water makes the workmen's feet very tough.

12

There are many small "family" salt farms like this one along Malta's rocky coast. Here the salt farmer and his sons are transferring seawater from large pools to smaller ones where the salt will form faster.

Here is a view from the air of a modern salt field in Brazil, S. A. Two types of ponds are always used. Water goes first to a large settling pond, then to smaller ponds sometimes called "garden ponds." It is in the smaller ponds that the salt is actually produced.

This field of seawater has been planted with sticks. This is one of the older methods not much in use anymore, but, if you look closely, you can see the salt beginning to form around the sticks in little circles. When the water is drained off this field, the salt around the sticks will look like giant mushrooms stuck on top of tree stumps.

From *Salt: The Fifth Element* by G. L. Eskew

This is a view of the solar ponds in Utah, U.S.A. Here the briny water of the Great Salt Lake is used to make salt.

Dams and dikes of earth and stone are used here in the Philippines to divide a salt farm into four big lots and many small ones. Workers are loading stones on rafts for use in building the dikes.

United Nations

The main saltwater entrance on a salt farm is called a
weir. Here, the weir is being opened to flood the lots
with fresh seawater.

This worker at a salt farm near Manila is making salt by the old method of transferring seawater from one lot to another, as the sun dries off the water. Newer methods using machinery can raise the output of salt from 35 tons to 100 tons for the same area.

17

These modern windmills are Dutch drainage pumps. They are being used at the Elephant Pass saltworks in Ceylon, where United Nations Technical Assistance experts are advising on modern saltmaking methods. The *solar* method is used to make most of our table salt. Human beings need about ¼ ounce of salt a day. If there were no salt at all, few men or animals could live much longer than a month.

Australian News and Information Bureau

The wet salt produced here in the south of Australia will be used as a raw material in the production of soda ash and caustic soda. Salt is very important to the chemical industry.

This brine pumped along the wooden runway, below, called a *race*, is dyed pink to make it absorb the sun's rays faster. Here, dripping from the boards, the salt which has begun to form looks like pink icicles.

Australian News and Information Bureau

United Nations

Many different things must be done to set up and run a large salt farm today. It is important, for example, that the salt beds be level. Here, and on the left, workers are surveying the land to be used.

Weather plays a big part in salt farming. Saltmakers have the same respect for weather that farmers have. This weather expert is taking a reading from one of the instruments set up at saltworks in Ceylon.

Here, a worker has climbed up to adjust a weather instrument. Salt farms need a hot, dry, windy climate. *Solar salt* is made by the action of sun *and* wind on water.

Saltmakers worry about rain. In some places where brine has been piped into wooden or iron vats and left in the sun, movable roofs are used to cover the vats. When rain comes, a big bell is rung that sounds like a fire alarm. Everyone, including the children in school, leaves what he is doing and rushes to roll the roofs over the salt.

23

Here, a worker tests another kind of weather instrument. In some countries, today, the large salt farms have a special arrangement with the official weather bureau. Rain forecasts are sent by cable directly to the saltworks. Quick action is then taken to cover the salt heaps.

If rain does come when the ponds are thick with salt, workers have to drain off the water. It is like skimming the cream
off a huge pan of milk. Here, in Jordan, along the northern
coast of the Dead Sea, a worker is making a report of con-
ditions in the beds. The Dead Sea, the Red Sea, and the
Great Salt Lake have the highest amount of salt, called *salt
content*, of any waters. Salt makes water very heavy. If you
were to try to swim in the Dead Sea, you would float like a
cork.

Here, in the Philippines, a worker is testing the salt content of some seawater. Usually about 250–300 gallons of seawater equal 70 pounds of salt. It takes 70 pounds of salt to make one bushel!

Here, some plans for new construction of evaporating ponds are being discussed. Salt farms need to cover large areas in order to produce the amount of salt needed today. Salt combines two elements: chlorine and sodium. Its chemical name is *sodium chloride*.

United Nations

Here, you can see some of the Dead Sea salt beds and a worker shoveling the salt that has formed (crystallized) as the water evaporated. To Hebrews the sea was the Salt Sea, for there was no animal or vegetable life in it.

A saltworker in Formosa smooths and evens off the brine in a flat pond. In the background you can see a hill of drying salt. This worker is all covered up for protection against the hot sun.

Here, you can see the openings in front of the hats that protect the workers from the sun. Being wrapped up like this also protects against mosquitoes, which like salt fields.

Salt is harvested in different ways in different countries. These workers at the salt flats at Salinas on the south coast of Puerto Rico are breaking up the salt with large picks.

31

United Nations

Above, salt is being harvested in India. Salt is one of India's most important products, and is also obtained there by running seawater into shallow tanks set up along the coast.

A tidy salt field in Portugal shows salt in various stages of drying.

Photo "Sni-Yan"

News Bureau, Spanish National Tourist Dept.

Mounds of drying salt cover a field in Spain. The longer salt is allowed to cure, the better. In both Spain and Russia there are also found natural hills of salt.

Australian News and Information Bureau

Here, in Australia, a tractor is used to level out the salt forming in the beds.

This is called a bucket elevator. It scoops up the salt and loads it at a rate of 40 tons an hour.

Australian News and Information Bureau

Here, on the Great Salt Lake in Utah, U.S.A., salt is being harvested as if it were a field of wheat. The Great Salt Lake is 80 miles long and an irregular 20 miles wide. American Indians used to make ceremonious treks to the lake to visit the "old witch salt woman," who they believed lived there.

These boys in the Philippines are carrying salt off the field
in the same way that it was carried hundreds of years ago.

Puerto Rico News Service

Wheelbarrows do the job here in Puerto Rico.

This man in Portugal carries the salt on his head.

Photo "Sni-Yan"

Here, in Jordan, you can see a type of one-rail cart that is used to carry salt off a field. The salt here will go to the plant (in the background) where it will be processed into potash. Potash is used as a fertilizer. Thirteen major chemicals come from salt and another 21 can be obtained when salt is processed by electricity.

Here, in a salt field in Sardinia, you can see the carts waiting to be loaded. Today, there are actually as many as 14,000 uses of salt. Only 5 percent is used for our food. There is salt in shoe leather and in the dye of a hat. It preserves meat and fish. It softens water. It is used in making glass and building roads, and even in the steel mills for "pickling" ingots. Salt is used in freezing, but is also a de-icer. Large amounts are used to melt heavy ice on our roads.

This is a two-track train used for carrying salt off the salt fields. This one is in Ceylon but it is similar to others in use throughout the world.

Pan American Union

Sometimes salt is bagged right on the field. You can imagine what hot work it must be at this salt field in Colombia, S. A., under the blazing sun.

Salt is often stockpiled in huge mountainous piles called bulk dumps.

Australian News and Information Bureau

Here, salt is being stacked by crane. At the left is the little train that brought the salt off the field.

Here, the crane has opened up and added several more tons
to a pile that will soon look like a small mountain.

43

News Bureau, Spanish National Tourist Dept.

These are workers in Spain loading railroad cars from a hill of salt.

These men in India are loading baskets with salt and the women are carrying it to the mill on their heads.

Information Service of India

Here, at the Hanku salt field in China, a belt conveyer loads salt for transport.

In Sardinia, Italy, another kind of conveyer carries
salt up and down.

At this salt mine in Senegal, Africa, we can see the mountains of salt; a truck bringing a new load; the conveyer belt; and, in the background, salt being bagged by workers.

This odd-looking train is in use in Northern Luzon in the Philippines. It is used for transporting salt at the Pacific Farms there. Transportation of salt over long distances has always been a major problem for the salt industry. Salt is bulky and costly to move, yet it cannot be priced too high, for all men need it. The closer salt is to its market, the better it is for the seller and the buyer.

This is a caravan in Afghanistan being loaded with salt. Man has always traveled great distances to buy or carry salt for sale. The old salt routes became roads, and the roads highways along which settlements grew. So salt is responsible for many a location of town or city. We know that the Via Salaria in Italy was built to bear caravans of salt from the works at Ostia to Rome. Salt was such a valuable product that Roman soldiers had to guard against robbery. The soldiers were paid in salt, and from this comes the word *salary*.

These fishermen in Noirmoutier, France, put their salt
to immediate use. The trawlers of the fishing fleet take
on loads to salt down their catch. Salt is obtained in
France from salt marshes or mines.

SALT
OF THE EARTH

The salt of the earth comes from brine wells, layers of rock salt deep in the earth, or from natural outcroppings like the pillar of salt (above) near Sdom in Israel. There are some other strange natural sources of salt. In Tunis, there is a small lake where in summer crusts of salt form so thick and hard that the people can walk over it as if on frozen ice. The salt is cut and sawed like ice. In Australia there are "salt bushes." In Java, there are mud volcanos which shoot out salt water along with mud. The people there gather the mud and boil out the salt.

This is a region in Afghanistan way off the beaten track of the world and very hard to get to. The nomads above are traveling through land covered with a layer of salt left there by the salty lakes of the region. In some other places of the world where soil is salty, the salt comes to the surface following rains. It is called *effloresced* salt, and can be seen on sand along the seashore sometimes in India, Africa, Russia, and Argentina.

This mountain is called Cerro de Sal, or Salt Mountain. It is near Barahona in the Dominican Republic and is one of the largest known "chunks" of salt in the world. This peak probably goes almost a half mile into the earth also.

53

This is a salt mountain in Jajikistan, U.S.S.R., and, below, a closer view of the salt outcroppings of the mountain. The name of this mountain is Hadja-Mumin.

Below is a diagram of a salt bed in Cheshire, England. Before the discovery of rock salt in Britain, salt was made from the brine of salt springs which came to the surface in a few places. It is believed that the Roman Legions first taught Britain how to boil spring brine in shallow lead pans to make white salt. There are written records of salt manufacture at Droitwich from the eighth century.

Courtesy ICI Information Service

GLACIAL DRIFT

SAND

MARL

MARL

MARL & SALT

SALT

MARL

MARL & SALT

MARL

SALT

SALT

SALT

MARL

SALT

MARL & SALT

SALT

These are salt slabs waiting for transportation to market at the port of Mopti, in Mali, Africa. The slabs were carried by camels from the Sahara to Timbuktu, and then by canoes to Mopti, which is on the Niger River. Centuries ago, among the great Sahara sights were the annual processions of camel caravans to the fabulous city of Timbuktu. Timbuktu was once the center of the salt trade and the wealthiest city in the world.

Here is a view of a salt mine where the very dry climate makes open-air mining possible. The salt is cut into loaves of about 75 pounds. These loaves are transported by donkeys, two to an animal.

Yugoslav Information Service

One method of mining rock salt much in use today, particularly in the United States, is to drill a well to a salt bed, pump water down to the salt and pump the saltwater solution (brine) back up to the surface. The brine is then processed in vacuum pans where the water boils off, leaving the pure crystal salt. The wells above are in Yugoslavia. Salt wells may be anywhere from 750 to 7,000 feet deep.

SALT DOME

OIL BEARING SAND—2475 FT.

NO. 2—2824 FT.

NO. 3—2908 FT.

NO. 1—4173 FT.

Standard Oil (N.J.)

This shows a cross section of a salt dome. A salt dome is a salt formation that keeps pushing out and upward under the earth like a big, odd-shaped underground balloon. When enormous pressure is put on salt it becomes plastic and flows, rising upward. Oilmen are most interested in the locations of salt domes because it has been discovered that oil and natural gas are often found nearby. Salt domes occur in the U.S.A. throughout the gulf of Texas, Louisiana, and Mississippi. About 250 are known to exist but it is likely there are many more.

This is a tunnel in a rock salt mine near Salzburg, Austria. Most industrial salt comes from direct mining in underground mines.

Here, 20-pound salt rocks are rolled out of the Barahona mine in the Dominican Republic, for transport to a crushing station. Mining of rock salt is similar in many ways to coal mining.

International Salt Company

(*Above*) These men are going down a mine shaft in an elevator and inspecting the walls on the way. Great salt beds underlie thousands of square miles in the U.S.A. The largest deposits are in Michigan, Ohio, New York, Pennsylvania, Kansas, Oklahoma, and Texas. (*Below*) The first operation in mining rock salt is called undercutting. This machine clears the side walls at floor level.

ICI Information Services

Holes about 10 feet deep and spaced at fixed distances are drilled in the salt wall (called the *mine face*). These holes will be filled with explosives.

These men are drilling holes working from a special platform.

Here, the powderman is loading and wiring the holes in the mine face. Blasts are timed to go off in a series one after the other.

After blasting, workers and machines move in and break up the salt into pieces to be fed onto a belt conveyer. Scientists say that salt deposits are the result of repeated evaporation (drying up through heat) of the waters of huge, ancient, inland seas.

Here, two Soviet miners use a different kind of drill in the Solotvin salt mines in the Ukraine, U.S.S.R. European countries have mined rock salt since the year 1000. The largest of the mines is the famous Wieliczka mine near Cracow, Poland.

This miner in Nova Scotia is testing a salt rock crack to make certain no dangerous edges are left hanging to harm the miners. The mineral name for salt is *halite*.

Now you can begin to see the size of the "rooms" which are being carved out of the salt mine. Here, a large tractor is at work moving the salt which has been blasted to the floor of the mine.

International Salt Company

Here you see the main chamber of a salt mine with sup-
porting pillars left to hold up the roof. The mine is beginning to look something like a crude cathedral. Later, you
will see how cathedrals have really been built in these
underground mines.

International Salt Company

Here is a view of the long conveyer belt that carries broken-up salt to an elevator shaft for hoisting to the top. When the salt reaches the surface, it will be graded and processed.

An inspector in an Austrian mine rides his bicycle down the conveyer-belt line of salt.

Salt mines are sometimes like huge underground cities. They are clean and the air clear, so much business can be done down below ground. This telephone is connected with other phones underground and with telephones on the surface; and when a foreman wants to inspect an operation he gets in a Jeep and drives there!

This is an underground machine shop in a mine in Louisiana, U.S.A. The shop is used to put together and repair mining equipment. Shafts in mines are usually too small to handle the large equipment used in salt mines, so parts of machines are lowered into the mine and put together there. Rock salt is so strong and hard that an ordinary pickax hardly dents it. Rock salt machines have to be very rugged.

This is an electrical control panel in a mine which covers over a square mile underneath the city of Detroit, Michigan, U.S.A. The mine's corridors are as wide as four-lane highways, and the ceilings as high as two-story buildings. The panel controls dozens of conveyer belts, crushers, and other machines.

74

British Information Services, London

On this main roadway of a British mine you can see the trucks carrying loads of salt. Notice the sidewalk at the side and the electric lights.

A small train is used in this Austrian mine to move salt rock to the surface. Years ago, donkeys were used to carry salt to the surface. The donkeys lived in the mines all the time.

Austrian Information Service

75

This man is on the surface. The panel he operates controls very complicated hoisting machinery. He is called a hoist engineer.

This is a view of the surface buildings where salt is processed and refined. This mine at Avery Island, Louisiana, U.S.A., was bitterly fought over by Union and Confederate troops during the Civil War in the United States. When Northern soldiers seized the island, burned and destroyed the buildings and flooded the salt pits, it was a severe loss to the South. The South already had problems making and transporting the salt needed to keep an army on the march. Salt has been an important factor in many wars, for salt is necessary to keep armies healthy and strong.

Standard Oil (N.J.)

A research laboratory in a salt refinery looks like this. Researchers look for new materials, new methods, new uses, and new products.

International Salt Company

Here, a foreman in the refinery runs a test on brine. Salt research affects many other fields: agriculture, photographic chemicals, biology, and engineering.

British Information Services

This is one of the oldest methods of processing salt from brine. It is called the open-pan method, and is similar to one of the methods used by early American colonists in the days when saltmaking was one of America's first industries.

This is a view of two modern evaporators in a vacuum evaporation plant in Britain. You can see how huge and complex machinery for refining salt has become.

British Information Services

These are vacuum tanks in Japan. The workman is checking the steam pressure.

William Rittase

These vacuum "pans" are in the United States. After the water has been evaporated, salt is taken out of the bottom part of these huge columns.

International Salt Company

A storage pile of rock salt waits for a pickup by highway departments. It will be used to keep the highways clear of ice.

United Press

In some places, rock salt is dumped into bins according to grade. Different grades and sizes will be used for different purposes. From these bins the salt will slide into railroad cars on a siding below.

These are large chemical storage tanks at a chlorine plant in West Virginia, U.S.A. The plant is located over a vast bed of rock salt. The salt is brought up as brine and then processed for use in manufacture of plastics, dyes, vitamins, and many other products.

Leonardo da Vinci's great painting, "The Last Supper," shows salt spilled before Judas. Salt was believed to be a protection against sickness and evil. In the Holy Land, salt was used for food and to preserve fish, olives, and hides. It came to have great importance in religious rites and customs of many nations. It was used to seal an agreement, for it was believed that two who ate salt together could not become enemies. Among the ancient Greeks, also, it was usual before each meal to present salt to the gods as an offering of thanks, and spilled salt was a bad omen. Salt has been used, also, at one time or another, in every country as a form of money.

Animals have always worn paths to salt licks. (*Lick* is the word we use for a place where natural salt is found.) Early man was a hunter and he followed the paths the animals took, looking for game. The trails became roads. In 1807, Daniel Boone or his sons marked an overland trail to a salt spring in central Missouri. That trail became Missouri's main east-west highway! Wild animals still beat paths through forests and fields to find salt, but these well-cared-for sheep get special blocks like the one below. They never eat more than they need.

Standard Oil (N.J.)

British Information Services,
London

Here is a salt silo where salt is stored in bulk. This silo holds 1,000 tons of salt.

Here you see all the buildings of a French mine in Alsace. Notice the railroad tracks that surround the front line of buildings. Salt is bulky and heavy and costly to transport.

French Embassy Press and Information Division

Rock salt being transported by cable from a mine in the
U.S.S.R.

British Information Services, London

This is bulk salt being loaded into a ship at Runcorn, England. Some historians say salt was the first and principal cargo of the Phoenicians, who carried salt from Spanish deposits and Palestinian ports near the Dead Sea to the Mediterranean cities for market.

Here a ship takes off with English salt in its hold. As late as 1900, English salt was sold in large amounts to the United States. It came as ballast on the ships which carried American produce back to England. Salt has been called the oldest article of commerce. It is said that even before the Roman invasion of England, Britons carried their crude salt by pack train from the mining area of Cheshire to southern England. High tides often forced the caravans to halt on the banks of the Thames River. A village grew up at the spot. The village became Westminster, the beginning of London.

British Information Services, London

Kansas Industrial Development Commission

Salt mines are very fine places for storage. In wartime many art treasures and other valuables were put in the European mines for protection against bombs and fire. Here some businessmen in Kansas, U.S.A., have built offices in a salt mine (there is even a kitchen), and are using the vast underground space as a center for storing important and valuable records. Salt is a sealer, also. So studies are being made to find out if atomic radioactive waste could be sealed off in layers of underground salt.

This is the Catedral de La Sal in the interior of a salt mine at Zipaquirá, Colombia, S. A. Mass is held more than a mile inside the earth. The church holds 5,000 people. This cathedral was built by the miners themselves and was blessed in 1950 by the Papal Nuncio of Colombia.

This is a view of the famous underground chapel in the Wieliczka salt mine in Poland. This mine has many subterranean (underground) hallways which contain chapels, music and dance halls, and many examples of sculpture, all carved out of natural rock salt.

INDEX

About the Author

ANITA BROOKS has been a free-lance magazine writer, a book editor and a private school teacher. She has traveled widely, on one occasion collaborating on an educational art project in Puerto Rico; on another assisting the director of the Sarah Lawrence College summer program in France.

In addition to her own active life, she has a family with three children.